BRITISH TREES IN WINTER

BRITISH TREES IN WINTER

BY

F. K. MAKINS, M.A., F.L.S.

Diploma of Forestry of the University of Oxford

LONDON

J. M. DENT AND SONS LIMITED

1945

ILLUSTRATIONS

Photographs of the following will be found between pages 12 and 13

PREFACE

IT is generally agreed that the fuller use of land made necessary by the present war must be continued after the war if Britain is to become less dependent on imports, and if unemployment is to be kept within reasonable limits. The growing of trees for timber and other useful products is a branch of husbandry as important in its way as farming. Forestry, therefore, must take a more prominent place in the economic life of the country. Trees must be cultivated for their uses as well as for beauty and sport. All this is recognized in the Report on Post-War Forest Policy issued by H.M. Forestry Commissioners. They have made proposals for increasing the area under woodland to five million acres in fifty years. At present there are three million acres, or five per cent of the total land area, a smaller percentage than that of any other European country. They also propose to form national forest parks and camping grounds. Such an ambitious programme will hardly be possible without the sympathy and understanding of the general public and of those not specially concerned with forestry. Love of trees is fairly widespread, but a little more knowledge would prevent certain abuses; for instance, carelessness with fires, nailing wire to trees, breaking down rabbit-netting, and tearing off whole boughs to get at a few flowers or berries. There is also a lot of misguided opposition to planting waste land with trees, opposition based on alleged interference with amenity, or mere sentiment. To plant exotic conifers in this country is not a sin against good taste; any one who has ever been in a mature wood of such trees will understand that. The process is bound to continue, because many valuable species grow better in our climate than in their own, and it will be a good thing to get acquainted with them. In course of time they will be as much British as the elm, the sycamore, and the horse-chestnut. It is just as short-sighted to object on principle to the felling of trees. Trees together form crops as much as fields of wheat or barley. They should be reaped at the right time, and replaced by planting, sowing, or natural regeneration. Unlike field crops, however, trees of different kinds and ages can be grown together and cut at different times. Thus, large clearances can be avoided. Groups or isolated specimens of special beauty or historical interest ought, in any case, to be allowed to stand for as long as they will.

This book is intended for the layman who wants to know about trees, as well as for the forester and timber merchant.

Correct identification is the key to all further knowledge. It is comparatively easy to identify trees in summer, when the leaves, flowers, and fruits can be had, and for the same reason, evergreens should present no great difficulty. Illustrations of all these can be seen in other works, including the author's *The Identification of Trees and Shrubs* (Dent, 1936). But a handy guide to deciduous trees in winter has been a long-felt want. Written descriptions are not very helpful unless supplemented by a key and clear illustrations of the twigs. Both have been provided. They will be found at the end of the book.

No attempt can be made in a work of this size to deal with all the exotic trees that may be grown in Britain. Every tree here described is either a native of Britain, or at one time or another has had a place in British forestry.

The authorities for the now accepted Latin names have been given in full, except that Linnaeus has been shortened to L.

F. K. M.

ABELE. *See* POPLAR.

ACACIA (*Robinia Pseudacacia* L.). The hardy tree commonly known as Acacia is not a true acacia. It is a native of North America, where it is called the Black Locust, and was introduced to this country in the seventeenth century largely to provide trenails for shipbuilding. In winter the appearance of the tree is stark and ugly, seldom growing straight, and with stiff tortuous branches. The brown bark is deeply furrowed. The crooked twigs are long, thinnish, and of a dark chocolate colour, ridged and warted. The leaf-scars are conspicuous and of irregular shape, flanked by two short straight spines, though sometimes these are absent. The buds are very small and surrounded by the leaf-scar. The wood is yellowish green, hard, heavy, and durable. It is difficult to get straight timber of any length, though a use has been found for it in sound-proofing. Though hard to split it yields good firewood, better than oak, though not so good as beech or ash.

ALDER (*Alnus glutinosa* L.). An inhabitant of the banks of streams and other moist places. The shape is usually broad at the base, narrowing gradually towards the top. It is easily recognized in winter by the violet-coloured stalked buds and the presence of small woody cone-like bodies and clusters of undeveloped catkins. The timber makes good plywood, while the poles are used for turnery. Though easy to split it gives poor firewood but good charcoal.

ALDER BUCKTHORN (*Rhamnus Frangula* L., *Frangula Alnus* Miller) is a shrub or small tree, and rather rare, except in fenny districts. In spite of its name it has no thorns. If the buds are looked at closely it will be noticed that they are made of tiny un-developed leaves not covered by bud-scales. The twigs are slender, reddish brown, and conspicuously streaked with lenticels. The wood yields a valuable charcoal much in demand during the war.

APPLE (*Malus* Miller). On those twigs which have grown vigorously in length during the past summer the buds are small, three-angled, and pressed close to the stem; on the shorter side shoots they are larger and egg-shaped; all are hairy and grow above a narrow crescent-shaped leaf-scar; under the hairs their colour is brown. The youngest twigs are reddish brown and glossy, with scanty clinging hairs. The short side shoots or 'spurs' are numerous and much ringed; in the wild crab apple they are sometimes tipped

9

with a spine. The wood does not split easily, carves well, and makes good wood-blocks for printing and engraving; it burns well and with a sweet scent.

ARBOR-VITAE is more commonly known by its scientific name, *Thuya* L. As in the cypresses the evergreen foliage consists of graceful flat fronds which on close examination are seen to be made up of opposite pairs of tiny scale leaves. The genus differs from cypress in the character of the cones, which in Thuya are all hinged to the base of the cone. Any attempt to distinguish the two by the foliage is bound to fail. There are several species, but the only one likely to be found in plantations is *Thuya plicata* Don (*T. gigantea* Nuttall), also known as *Thuya Lobbii* by nurserymen and gardeners. This is the American Red Cedar. It was introduced to this country by Messrs. Veitch through their collector William Lobb in 1853. It grows fast into a tall narrow tree with an erect leading shoot. The trunk is buttressed, and has a red bark fissured into scaly ridges. The foliage when crushed or torn gives out a pleasant scent of pineapple or lemon. The cones are narrowly egg-shaped, rather like a Grecian urn. The tree bears shade and can be used for underplanting. It also makes an excellent hedge because it is hardy, grows fast, and stands clipping; young plants can be raised easily from cuttings. The timber is greyish brown, tough, and durable. It is largely used on the Pacific coast of North America for roof shingles, boats, weather-boarding, fencing, telegraph poles, and gates; in fact, for any purpose where the timber has to stand up to severe weather outside. Being such a valuable and accommodating tree it should be planted more extensively in this country, though it is liable to be attacked by a fungus disease, especially in nurseries. The wood burns well, with an aromatic scent.

ASH (*Fraxinus excelsior* L.). Bark pale grey, rough in old trees but smooth in young ones, in which it is often tinged with yellow or bronze. The colour of the blaze is a light buff. The winter silhouette can be recognized by the stout twigs which turn upward at the ends of the drooping branches. Horse chestnut also has this feature, but differs in other respects. The smooth, silver-grey twigs of ash are unmistakable by their black stumpy buds in opposite pairs. The terminal bud is much larger than the lateral ones, its outer scales being stout and keeled. The leaf-scars are large and somewhat U-shaped or helmet-shaped. Natural seedlings are produced in abundance, but largely eaten or gnawed by rabbits. The tree yields one of our most valuable timbers, being strong and elastic, therefore suitable for aircraft construction, tool handles, sports goods, shafts, felloes, and coach-building. The wood is light-coloured, with little distinction between heart and sapwood. The poles make good rails, while the saplings are split lengthwise for making sheep-cribs and the shores of hurdles. The firewood is excellent, splits easily, burns slowly, and gives out a lot of heat even when green. Ugly black lumps on the stem are caused by a canker; infected trees should be cut out and burnt.

ASPEN. *See* POPLAR.

BEECH (*Fagus sylvatica* L.). The crown is dense, made up of countless ascending or horizontal branches ending in fine zigzag twigs. Few plants can grow under its shade. The bark is pale grey and smooth, often green with moss or lichen; small woody lumps are sometimes found on it, these are caused by a gall insect, and do not affect the timber. When the bark shows a corrugated surface the condition is probably caused by the healing up of local injuries. The appearance of a white deposit indicates the attack of a scale insect, which is not in itself particularly dangerous; healthy trees usually recover, but sickly ones may die. Being so numerous the branches sometimes fuse together, giving remarkable effects. The winter buds are long, narrow, and pointed, and bright chestnut-brown. Their arrangement on the twig is *distichous*, i.e. in two rows causing the leaves to spread out on either side in one flat plane. The dead leaves persist throughout the winter on young trees and hedge plants, and often on the lower branches of big trees. Their warm brown is an asset to the winter landscape. On the ground they take a long time to rot, often forming thick layers through which nothing can grow. Good seed years happen infrequently, but a few prickly husks split into four can usually be seen on large trees throughout the winter. The timber is almost white when fresh felled, with no distinction between heart and sapwood, but later the heartwood turns light brown: it is useful for furniture, carpenters' tools, shoe-trees and heels, paving blocks and mangle-rollers, and there is, at the time of writing, a demand for clean cylindrical stems for veneering into aircraft plywood. It takes creosote well, and when impregnated under pressure can be used for railway sleepers; untreated, it does not last long in the ground. The wood splits easily and makes good firewood, green or dry. The charcoal is not of much value.

BIRCH (*Betula* L.). Every one knows the graceful white stems and long, drooping, whip-like branches of the common birch, but less well known is the fact that there are two distinct species native to Great Britain.

The Silver Birch (*Betula pendula* Roth) is the commoner but less valuable of the two. The twigs are warted and hairless. Often the bark does not become white until the tree has passed the sapling stage, and the writer has noticed quite large trees without any white bark at all; it peels off in papery layers except at the base of the trunk where it is usually rough and corky, with deep fissures.

The White Birch (*Betula pubescens* Ehrhart), sometimes called Swedish Birch, grows faster, taller, and straighter, and is brilliant white from early on. The twigs are downy and not warted.

Innumerable hybrids occur between the two. Birches spring up naturally on commons, heaths, and waste land wherever there are mother trees to give seed, and may become a troublesome weed. The male catkins appear in autumn and hang on the trees all winter. The female catkins do not develop until spring.

Birch splits badly but yields good firewood, which, however, burns too quickly; it also makes good charcoal. Poles of three inches in diameter or more are valued for turnery: for this purpose Swedish birch is more in demand. Birch plywood is imported in large quantities.

BLACKTHORN (*Prunus spinosa* L.). The black thorny twigs are well known in our hedges, especially when the white blossom appears before the leaves in a spell of sunny, but dry, cold weather in late winter—'blackthorn winter' as it is called. Many country-men think the twigs are poisonous because the thorns are apt to break off at the tips and bury themselves in the skin, where they fester. Like hawthorn, it has to be kept low to form a hedge, but if allowed to grow it makes a pretty tree, quite as good as many so-called 'choice' species of Prunus seen in gardens; to get the best result all the suckers must be removed, for it suckers far more freely than hawthorn. The fruit of blackthorn is the Sloe. Near relatives are the Bullace or Damson (*Prunus insititia* L.) and the Plum (*Prunus domestica* L.), both of which are occasionally seen wild in hedges. Apart from being less thorny it is difficult to distinguish them from blackthorn until they flower and fruit.

BOX (*Buxus sempervirens* L.) is said by Professor A. G. Tansley to be truly native at Boxhill near Dorking in Surrey, near Little Kimble in Buckinghamshire, and at Boxwell in the southern Cots-wolds. Elsewhere it appears to have been planted as cover for pheasants. Notice the small oval leaves in opposite pairs, which distinguish it from all other evergreens outside gardens, except possibly privet, which is half evergreen. The branchlets are four-angled, while those of privet are cylindrical. The little yellowish-green flowers in the angles of the leaves can often be seen as early as February. The wood is yellow, hard, heavy and true, difficult to split; it would be in greater demand for mathematical and musical instruments, printing blocks, chessmen, and so on if it could be obtained in larger quantities and of sufficient size. Pliny describes it as being as hard to burn as iron, producing no flame, and totally

ACACIA

ASH

BEECH

ACACIA

BEECH

BIRCH

CEDAR OF LEBANON

LAWSON'S CYPRESS

ASH

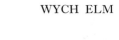

WYCH ELM

BIRCH

CEDAR OF LEBANON

WYCH ELM

DOUGLAS FIR

SWEET CHESTNUT

DOUGLAS FIR

COMMON ELM

HORNBEAM

HORSE CHESTNUT

HORSE CHESTNUT   LIME

LARCH   COMMON ELM

LARCH

LIME

MOUNTAIN ASH

OAK

OAK (in age)

MOUNTAIN ASH

OAK (in vigour)

SCOTS PINE

PLANE

GREY POPLAR or ABELE

24

SILVER FIR

LOMBARDY POPLAR

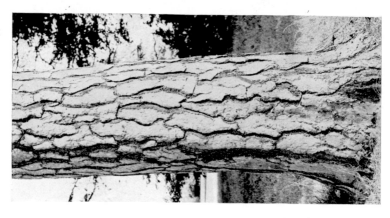

SCOTS PINE

SILVER FIR

SPRUCE

SWEET CHESTNUT

PLANE POPLAR

HOLM OAK

SYCAMORE

WILLOW

WALNUT

SYCAMORE

WALNUT

WHITE WILLOW

unfit for charcoal. According to J. C. Loudon it is the only European wood that will sink in water. For hedges and topiary work the tree has been cultivated since Roman times.

BUCKTHORN (*Rhamnus catharticus* L.) is not so uncommon as is generally supposed, for it is easily overlooked in the tangle of a hedge, having inconspicuous flowers and fruits. It counts as a thorny tree though the thorns are few. It is easily distinguished by the buds being 'sub-opposite,' that is, nearly, but not quite, opposite to each other on the twigs. The inner bark is a strong cathartic —hence the Latin epithet *catharticus*—also the bluish-black berries, which have a nasty taste.

CEDAR (*Cedrus* Link), though not native, is too conspicuous a feature in many parts of the British landscape to be ignored.

The Cedar of Lebanon (*Cedrus libanotica* Link), introduced in the seventeenth century, is the best known, with its tufts of bluish-green needles and large flat-topped crown.

There is also the Atlas Cedar (*Cedrus atlantica* Manetti), which differs slightly in the shape of its large fat cones which are cylindrical rather than egg-shaped, and in its leading shoot which is stiff and erect. It was first planted in Britain about the middle of last century.

The Himalayan Cedar or Deodar (*Cedrus deodara* Loudon), introduced into Britain by the Hon. W. Leslie Melville in 1831, has drooping branches and leading shoot.

The cones of all three are large and erect, their thin scales being superimposed like the leaves of a book. When the scales have fallen the axis of the cone remains erect on the branch. Cedar wood is light and durable but not strong. It is easy to work, but is filled with an essential oil which permeates the air all round. The scent of this oil, though pleasant at first, can become almost nauseating in time, and upsets some people; its presence, however, makes a cedar-wood chest absolutely moth-proof. The firewood is inferior.

CHERRY (*Prunus avium* L.), meaning not the fruit tree, but the Wild Cherry, Gean, or Mazard, occurs frequently in woods on limestone soils, and when covered with blossom in spring is a beautiful sight. The bark of young trees is somewhat similar to that of birch, peeling in horizontal strips, though of darker colour, with prominent horizontal lenticels. The twigs are stout, the buds egg-shaped, pointed, reddish brown, and clustered on the very short side shoots which are markedly ringed by the previous years' growth. The wood makes good furniture, being soft, easily worked, and taking a fine polish. Like apple and lime it carves well and makes good engraving blocks. The logs season best when stood on end. The firewood splits badly; it burns well when green but too quickly when dry.

Bird Cherry (*Prunus Padus* L.) occurs wild in the north and is sometimes planted in gardens in the south. It is a small tree, with the characteristic peeling bark of a cherry and slender purplish-brown twigs spotted with white lenticels. The winter buds are small, pointed, and light brown. The wood is hard and yellowish, with a disagreeable smell when fresh cut, and beautifully veined, especially if cut obliquely across the log (Loudon), but in this country large logs are unobtainable.

The Wild Dwarf Cherry (*Prunus Cerasus* L.) is rare and cannot be distinguished from the foregoing until the leaves and flowers open. It is usually a shrub not more than six or eight feet high, though it is capable of growing much bigger.

CHERRY LAUREL (*Prunus Laurocerasus* L.), a native of south-eastern Europe, was introduced as a thing of beauty at the end of the sixteenth century, since when it has taken such a firm hold that it has become 'too much of a good thing.' The smooth green stems branching in all directions and the glossy persistent leaves give a monotonous effect, and are a troublesome obstacle when walking through a wood. The wood burns well and makes good fence posts whenever straight enough lengths can be found. Cutting it down will not eradicate the cherry laurel; the only way to get rid of it is to uproot and burn.

CHESTNUT. *See* HORSE CHESTNUT *and* SPANISH CHESTNUT.

CYPRESS (*Cupressus* L.). Lawson's Cypress (*Cupressus Lawsoniana* J. A. Murray), though mostly seen in gardens, has strong claims as a forest tree. It was introduced in 1854 by Mr. William Murray, who sent seeds to Messrs. Lawson of Edinburgh. The foliage is similar to that of arbor-vitae though denser, darker, and less aromatic, while the leading shoot bends over in a graceful curve. The cones are globular, about the size of marbles or smaller; the cone-scales are spurred on the outer surface and *peltate*, i.e. attached to the stalk by the middle or whole of the inner surface. Imported timber of this species is known in the trade as Port Orford Cedar. C. P. Ackers says: The timber is by far the highest priced of all the conifers of the Pacific States,' adding: 'It is one of the most lasting trees we have in contact with the soil and so should be most useful for English estate work. Its great value is, however, in its use for battery separators.'

The only other cypress worth mentioning is the well-known Macrocarpa (*Cupressus macrocarpa* Hartweg), introduced from

California in 1838 by Mr. A. B. Lambert. The foliage is greener and not flattened. The cones are nearly as big as golf balls. It makes a fast-growing hedge, but is difficult to transplant except in pots. Most macrocarpa hedges are too severely clipped, with the result that they brown off in patches. The timber splits too easily to be of much value but makes good kindling wood.

DOGWOOD (*Cornus sanguinea* L.), common on soils containing lime, is more a bush than a tree, though it can grow to a height of thirty feet. The buds are opposite each other on the twigs, which are usually red and brighten the hedges in winter. It is sometimes known as Skewer Wood, from one of its uses. On the whole, the wood is of no value, though it gives excellent fuel and charcoal.

DOUGLAS FIR (*Pseudotsuga taxifolia* Britton) is favoured by British foresters owing to its rapid growth in this climate and high volume production wherever the conditions suit it. It was discovered near the Pacific coast of North America by Archibald Menzies in 1795 and introduced by David Douglas, collector to the Horticultural Society, in 1827. At first glance it can be confused with spruce and silver fir, but its pointed, beech-like buds and three-pronged bracts to the cone-scales mark it from spruce, while its hanging cones show it is not a silver fir. In saplings the bark is smooth but becomes rough in older trees. The blaze is yellow mottled with brown. It is unsuitable for coverts. Imported timber is known to the trade as Oregon Pine or British Columbian Pine. When the timber first appeared on the market it was thought to be a species of silver fir, of which the timber is nothing like so valuable as that of pines; actually Douglas fir is the equal, if not the superior of most pines, hence this perfectly legitimate trick to overcome trade prejudice. It is strong and durable, but does not hold nails well, and is almost as good as larch for rustic poles, fencing, and estate work. Many plantations have recently been cut down to provide pit props for the coal mines. The wood splits easily and burns well.

ELDER (*Sambucus nigra* L.) has loose opposite buds and warted pithy shoots which give out a sickly smell when cut. The heartwood is hard, heavy, and durable, and makes good stakes. It burns well when dry, but in remote country districts there is a superstitious objection to burning it indoors.

ELM (*Ulmus* L.) is a tall tree with rough bark giving a chocolate-coloured blaze. The winter buds are small, almost black, and approximately distichous. The small reddish flowers appear before the leaves, sometimes as early as February, in clusters on the previous year's twigs.

The so-called Common Elm or English Elm (*Ulmus procera* R. A. Salisbury) is said to have been introduced by the Romans. It has heavy side branches stepped up the trunk to give a stately terraced effect and ending in masses of erect twigs. Those twigs which arise directly from the trunk are usually corky. The English elm is primarily a tree of hedgerows and fields rather than of woods, and gives to the pastoral landscape of the southern and midland counties its typical English character. In the north and east it is absent or replaced by other species of elm. As the seed is rarely fertile reproduction is effected by numerous suckers. The timber is brown and strong, splits with difficulty, lasts well under water or completely buried in the ground, so that it is in demand for ship-building, dock construction, well kerbs, and coffins, and makes good rough weather-boarding, wheelbarrows, chair seats, ammunition and tinplate boxes, and railway sleepers.

In the eastern counties it is replaced by the Smooth-leaved Elm (*Ulmus nitens* Moench) and the Small-leaved Elm (*Ulmus minor* Miller). The former is not unlike the common English elm; according to H. Gilbert-Carter it is easily known at a distance by its fine pendulous spray. The latter, called in the eastern counties the Lock Elm because the hard wood locks the saw, rarely exceeds sixty feet, and has slender, wiry, interlacing twigs.

The Lock Elm of the midlands has been described by Dr. R. Melville under the name of *Ulmus Plotii* Druce as 'a graceful erect tree up to 100 feet in height, usually with arching leading shoot and at irregular intervals a few relatively short almost horizontal branches from which slender pendulous wiry branchlets descend, sometimes for many feet.'

The Wych Elm (*Ulmus glabra* Hudson) has a stringy bark and long spreading branches drooping at the ends and giving a broad domed crown. Its seed is fertile and it never suckers. The twigs are never corky. It is commonest in the west and north, and is often found in woods. The timber is white, strong, and elastic, having properties approaching those of ash, and makes good shafts, tool handles, and drop-hammer helves. Since the outbreak of the 1939 war it has been used in lifeboat construction.

The Cornish and Jersey Elms (*Ulmus stricta* Lindley) of the south-west have short erect branches, and are easily recognized by the narrow shape approximating that of the Lombardy poplar.

The Huntingdon Elm (*Ulmus vegeta* Schneider) also has upright branches, but the crown is broader.

Dutch Elm (*Ulmus hollandica* Miller) is a cross between wych and smooth-leaved elm. Its leaves and fruit resemble wych elm, but its bark and twigs are those of smooth-leaved. It suckers freely and has corky twigs. The timber is white.

All the elms hybridize and the hybrids are often difficult to identify.

Elm gives good firewood when dry, but in a fresh state it burns slowly and gives out little heat.

GUELDER ROSE (*Viburnum Opulus* L.), so called because it is supposed to have come originally from Guelderland in the Low Countries, can scarcely be called a tree as it rarely exceeds twelve feet. The buds are in opposite pairs, hairless and shining, on smooth twigs and enclosed by only one visible scale. Like its close relative, the wayfaring tree, it is commonest on lime-bearing soils.

HAWTHORN (*Crataegus monogyna* Jacques) is the main constituent of our hedges, but is capable of growing into a tree of twenty-five feet or more. As a hedge plant it is commonly called Quick; as a tree, May. The thorns are stiff and woody and up to an inch long, each thorn being in reality a branch, so that it appears directly above a leaf-scar. In this respect it is like blackthorn, but the leaf-scars are much narrower. The wood is white, hard, and difficult to work, but makes excellent firewood even when green and splits easily.

HAZEL (*Corylus Avellana* L.) is useful in spring for making pea-sticks, wattle hurdles, and thatching spars, and again in autumn when the nuts ripen. The blunt round buds are more or less distichous, though this character is sometimes difficult to determine in vigorous young shoots growing direct from a cut stool. The catkins or 'lambs'-tails' hang in the hedges all the winter; they are composed of the male flowers and shower their pollen in early spring. The females look like buds, but are tipped with a minute brush of scarlet. Hazel is commonly seen in open oak woods as an under storey, for it used to be cut back to the ground regularly every ten years or so, to spring up again from the stump and give whippy wands for hurdle and spar making. This industry is dying out for various reasons, so that much of our hazel underwood has grown too big and crooked to be of any value except for firewood, though it provides good cover for game.

HEMLOCK. *See* SPRUCE.

HOLLY (*Ilex Aquifolium* L.), with its stiff prickly leaves and scarlet berries, is too well known to need much description. Some trees have flowers with stamens only and so cannot produce berries. The wood is ivory-white, very hard, and heavier than any other British wood except box, like which it can be used for mathematical and musical instruments and printing blocks. It takes stain readily, and when dyed black can be substituted for ebony. The best way to season the logs is to strip off the bark and stand them on end.

HOLM OAK. *See* OAK.

HORNBEAM (*Carpinus betulus* L.) might be called a poor relation of beech. It has the same smooth bark and narrow-pointed buds in two ranks on the twig, but the buds are angled, much shorter, and without the bright chestnut-brown colour. The trunk is not cylindrical but irregular in section. Large trees are uncommon. Like the beech it stands a lot of shade, and can be planted under oak and ash and cut back again and again if desired, without killing it out. The wood is white, hard, and heavy, only box and holly being heavier; it is used for mallet heads, wood screws, pulleys, bobbins, machine cogs, and skittles. It is exceedingly strong. As firewood it is first class and makes excellent charcoal.

HORSE CHESTNUT (*Aesculus Hippocastanum* L.) is another successful introduction from south Europe about the middle of the sixteenth century. Its stout twigs, large gummy end buds, and clear leaf-scars make it a favourite for demonstration purposes. The winter outline is not unlike ash, but the bark is greenish, scaly, and often twisted, while the branchlets are heavier and more numerous. The wood is very white and soft; in central Europe it is used for toy making. The bark is now required by the makers of glucoside aesculin, which is a diagnostic reagent for bovine mastitis. The firewood is poor.

JUNIPER (*Juniperus communis* L.) is a coniferous evergreen bush or small tree with small bluish-black berries instead of cones. The sharp-pointed awl-shaped needles are in threes; each needle has a broad grey band on its upper surface, and is jointed at the base. Juniper is found mainly in the south of England on chalk downs, where it has the habit and appearance of gorse, but according to Professor Tansley it occurs also in the pine and birch woods of the Scottish highlands. The wood is light, yellowish brown, and scented, and makes good fuel.

LARCH (*Larix decidua* Miller) is our only deciduous conifer if you leave out the cultivated swamp cypress. It is believed to have been introduced into this country from the Alps early in the seventeenth century, though extensive plantations were not made until a hundred years later. The trunk is tall, thin, and straight, giving off horizontal branches at irregular intervals; it has a rough, scaly bark, giving a pinkish-brown blaze shot with purple. The young twigs are straw-yellow and conspicuously marked with the numerous spirally arranged leaf-bases. The older twigs often carry the small thin-scaled cones. The little globular buds are disposed at a wide angle to the twig. The timber is light, strong, and durable, having a larger proportion of heartwood than most others, hence it is valuable for fencing, pit props, and rustic poles. Planks from larger trees are in demand for boat-skins, and the peeled trunks make good masts and telegraph poles. In fact, larch is one of our most valuable and profitable trees, though many plantations are disfigured by canker. If plantations are thinned early and often so as to give the best trees plenty of head room, they will grow at a phenomenal rate on favourable soils and suffer little from canker.

The Japanese Larch (*Larix Kaempferi* C. S. Sargent) grows even faster when young, and is seldom attacked by canker and needs less thinning. It differs from the Common or European Larch in having reddish-brown twigs. There is no reason to suppose that the timber is any inferior. It was introduced by Messrs. Veitch in 1861.

Larch firewood gives out a good heat, but it does not light easily, crackles and sparks, and will go out before the wood is half consumed if the fire is left unattended.

LAUREL. *See* CHERRY LAUREL.

LIME (*Tilia vulgaris* Hayne) is a tall tree with smooth greenish bark rougher than that of beech, and giving a light brown blaze. The smooth cylindrical twigs are stiff and moderately thick, often red, and the buds distichous. Each bud has two scales, one large and one small. A characteristic but undesirable feature of lime is the great masses of twigs which appear wherever the tree has suffered damage, so much so that it is often difficult to get near enough to the trunk to put a tape round. The young shoots are useful for tying up faggots; another advantage is that rabbits do not like them. The only true native is the Small-leaved Lime (*Tilia cordata* Miller); Common Lime is a cross between it and *Tilia platyphyllos* Scopoli, which has downy twigs. The timber of lime is pale yellow or white, close-grained, light, and smooth; it is strong but not durable in the open; it does not split easily, and is good for carving, turnery, toy-making, glove-cutting boards, musical instruments, frames for bee-hives, and for shaping and modelling work such as model aeroplanes and ships for experimental purposes. The firewood is inferior.

MAPLE (*Acer campestre* L.), by which is meant the Common or Field Maple of hedges and coppices. (For other maples see Norway Maple and Sycamore.) A small tree with a straight trunk and rough, but not deeply fissured, bark. Winter buds small, in opposite pairs on tawny twigs, which are often corky. It is a common constituent of hedges as it stands clipping well. The wood is difficult to split, though it burns well and makes good charcoal. The tree is rarely big enough to yield timber, which is white, compact, fine-grained, and takes a high polish, being as good as sycamore.

MOUNTAIN ASH (*Sorbus Aucuparia* L.), also called Rowan,

19

grows at higher altitudes than any other native tree except birch. The stem is straight, grey, and smooth-barked. The twigs are stout and the winter buds large, blackish, and tufted with white hairs at the end. It is a good tree for small gardens, apart from its flowers and berries, because it grows in any soil, seldom exceeds thirty feet, never loses its shape, and attracts thrushes and blackbirds. Suckers appear at the base, it is true, but do not spread. The wood is nearly all heart and therefore durable; it burns well and makes good charcoal.

NORWAY MAPLE (*Acer platanoides* L.). Like the so-called Norway spruce this tree is not of strictly Norwegian origin. It was introduced from the continent of Europe in the seventeenth century, and is better looking than its near relatives the field maple and the sycamore. The bark is grey, with short shallow cracks and showing no tendency to form scales. The reddish buds are in opposite pairs on smooth brown twigs streaked with grey. The wood is white and much like that of sycamore.

OAK (*Quercus* L.). Common English Oak (*Quercus Robur* L.) has a deeply furrowed, corky bark giving a reddish-brown blaze. The winter silhouette is unmistakable: a gentle rounded top, heavy branches leaving the trunk at a wide angle and taking many sharp turns to end in stout aggressive twigs crowned by clusters of light brown buds. The timber has the characteristic silver grain possessed by no other common species; besides being good to look at it is hard, heavy, and strong, and by and large is the most valuable of our native timbers. The following are only a few of the uses to which it is put: shipbuilding, docks, lock-gates, railway wagons and sleepers, military lorries, beds for heavy machinery, battery containers for armoured vehicles, the arms of telegraph poles, barrel staves, ladder rungs, parquet flooring, panelling, furniture, and fencing. The timber splits easily, and cleft-oak fence posts last longer than sawn. Fortunately there is no shortage, so many trees having been planted by our forbears in Napoleonic times to provide timber for the navy. The firewood is excellent when dry. The best timber is obtained from alluvial soils and other low-lying situations, especially on clay. The bark of English oak was in demand for tanning until ousted by the South American quebracho woods, which contain a much higher percentage of tannin. The bark was stripped in spring from young oaks grown from stool and cut back every twenty years or so, and also from logs felled for timber. Most of the areas grown specially for bark are now derelict; some of them have been used since 1939 for the manufacture of pit props and charcoal. Oak bark can still be sold for £5 to £6 a ton. Galls, or 'oak apples,' contain a higher percentage of tannin than the bark.

The Durmast Oak (*Quercus sessiliflora* R. A. Salisbury) is a more symmetrical tree with a taller and straighter trunk, and can do with less lime in the soil than the common oak. The silver grain in the timber is less marked.

Turkey Oak (*Quercus Cerris* L.), a native of south-eastern Europe, was introduced at the beginning of the eighteenth century and planted largely in the south and west. Its rapid growth, great size, and good shape raise false hopes, as the timber is inferior. In winter it can be distinguished from ordinary oak by the deeper and more regular fissures in the bark, its hairy buds surrounded by thread-like stipules, and by the long, sharply toothed leaves that lie under the tree. Since 1939 it has been bought by merchants for conversion into sub-standard grade railway sleepers. An interesting cross between it and the Cork Oak (*Quercus suber* L.) is the Lucombe Oak (*Quercus lucombeana* Robert Sweet), frequently planted in the west of England. It is nearly an evergreen. The timber is of no value.

Holm Oak or Evergreen Oak (*Quercus Ilex* L.) is a native of south Europe and was introduced in the seventeenth century. It is an evergreen tree with a smooth or scaly light grey bark and a dense compact head. The leaves are from one to three inches long, pointed, dark green above and yellowish or whitish underneath. The acorns are small and about half enclosed by the cup. One seldom sees a tree damaged by wind, lightning, or disease. The heartwood is brown, as hard and heavy as hornbeam, and can be used for the same purposes. The firewood is excellent, burning slowly and quietly with glowing embers.

PEAR (*Pyrus communis* L.) is now rare in the wild state. In winter it is very like apple, though the crown is more elongated and the buds are dark brown and hairless. The branches are often thorny. The wood is heavy, fine-grained, and slightly tinged with red; like apple, it is good for carving and engraving-blocks, and makes excellent fuel and charcoal.

PINE (*Pinus* L.). Needles long and very thin, in bundles of two to five on very short shoots which are sheathed at the base. The cones have thick woody scales. Young trees are erect and pointed, the branches issuing in whorls. As there is one whorl to each year's growth the age of young trees can easily be ascertained.

The best known is the Scots Pine or Scotch Fir (*Pinus sylvestris* L.), which is probably the most beautiful tree in the winter landscape. The needles are in pairs, seldom more than three inches long and of a bluish-green colour, especially when seen from a distance. The bark of old trees splits into thick, corky plates which give a reddish-striped blaze. Higher up the trunk the bark becomes scaly, and finally smooth and reddish or orange-red. The crown is pointed during the time the tree is growing in height, it then flattens out.

The true Scots pine of the Highlands keeps its pyramidal shape longer, and finally becomes dome-shaped rather than flat. The timber is known to the trade as Red Deal or Yellow Deal. Being light and strong it is used mostly in building. Small straight trunks are peeled, creosoted under pressure, and used for telegraph posts. Young poles are peeled and cross-cut into pit props. For all these purposes the timber was imported from the Baltic in enormous quantities before 1939, since when we have had to use up most of our home plantations. Fortunately the most picturesque groups have been spared, largely because the timber in them does not amount to much, either in quantity or quality. The firewood smokes a lot, but is easy to light and therefore good for kindling.

Corsican Pine (*Pinus nigra* Arnold) is a common sight in the south of England. The needles are also in pairs but much longer and the whole tree darker and denser. The bark is never red. Notice the winter buds: they are shouldered at the end and thickly coated with white. It grows well on shallow calcareous soils over chalk and limestone. The Austrian Pine is a denser and greener variety. Dr. Henry used to say you could see through Corsican but not through Austrian. Both are excellent trees for wind-belts. The timber is like that of Scots though not so good. They came here in the eighteenth century.

Cluster Pine (*Pinus Pinaster* Aiton) is seen on the south coast, especially near Bournemouth, and is often planted. The needles are in pairs, very rigid, and up to eight inches long. The cones are large and clustered, hence the name. Most of the pit props used in South Wales came from forests of this tree on the sandy wastes south of Bordeaux, but with the fall of France in 1940 the traffic was cut off. After tapping the trunks for turpentine the French used to cut them into pit props and ship them to South Wales in returning coal ships.

A very rapid grower in the south and west is the Monterey Pine (*Pinus radiata* Don), usually called Insignis after its old Latin name *Pinus insignis* Douglas. It has two or three needles to each bundle, of a bright grass green. Young trees grow very fast and in mild situations make good windbelts. In fifty years an isolated specimen will reach a great size, with a broad spreading crown and usually several main stems. According to C. P. Ackers the timber is light and moderately strong, and makes good packing cases and butter boxes. It has been much planted in South Africa and New Zealand. The tree was introduced from the coast of California by David Douglas in 1833.

Among the pines with five needles in each bundle two are worth noticing: Weymouth Pine (*Pinus Strobus* L.) and Himalayan or Blue Pine (*Pinus excelsa* Wallich), both very much alike. The bark of young trees is smooth and slate-coloured, but roughens into small plates as they get thicker; if cut it exudes a crystal-clear watery resin filled with sugar. The needles hang down. It is almost impossible to distinguish the two when they are not growing side by side. The best way is to look at the cones if available; in Weymouth pine they are pointed at the tip, in the other rounded (Marshall Ward); also the twigs of Weymouth are practically hairless. Weymouth pine is a native of eastern North America and was introduced into England in 1705. A fashion for planting it was set up by Lord Weymouth, at Longleat, in Wiltshire, but the plantations were ravaged by disease. The timber is valuable and is known to the trade as Quebec Pine or Yellow Pine; it is widely used for every purpose in its native home and imported in large quantities to this country. The timber of the blue pine is also good. The firewood is rather better than that of the two-needled pines.

PLANE (*Platanus acerifolia* Willdenow). The London Plane is a cross between the American Buttonwood (*Platanus occidentalis* L.) and the Oriental Plane (*Platanus orientalis* L.). Apart from the striking white patches on the trunk identification is made easy by the conical one-scaled winter buds standing well out from the twig and almost completely enclosed by the narrow leaf-scar. The wood is yellowish-white and smooth-grained and can be used for veneer, furniture, motor bodies, and wheel hubs. The firewood is good.

POPLAR (*Populus* L.). The best known is the Lombardy Poplar (*Populus nigra*, variety *italica* Du Roi), which is a tall narrow tree owing to the branches growing almost vertical. It is useless for timber or firewood, but gives a pleasing effect on level ground. It is really a native of western Asia, whence it came to Italy, and to Britain about the middle of the eighteenth century.

Abele or Grey Poplar (*Populus canescens* J. E. Smith) has a whitish-grey bark, smooth at first, but later becoming rough at the base. In large trees the upper part of the trunk and the branches are pale grey and marked with horizontal rows of large lenticels shaped like conventional fir-trees. The buds and young twigs are cottony.

Aspen (*Populus tremula* L.) can be identified in winter by its pointed hairless buds turning inward toward the shining pale brown twigs. The bark is like that of the grey poplar.

Black Italian Poplar (*Populus serotina* Hartog) is a hybrid and bears only male catkins. These are red and make a fine show in early spring. The bark is rough and stringy. Mr. Gilbert-Carter says: 'Its fan-like crown is so unlike that of any other of our trees that students can soon learn to distinguish it at a distance of more than a mile.' It has sticky long-pointed buds on angular twigs.

23

Black Poplar (*Populus nigra* L.) is comparatively rare. The winter silhouette is like that of ash. The trunk and branches are usually swollen with large burrs.

The timber of all poplars is white and soft, that of grey poplar producing a woolly surface when sawn. It is difficult to split and burns slowly, giving little heat. It is therefore suitable for match sticks, pencils, chip baskets, packing cases, waggon bottoms, and high-grade pulp. Since 1939 a further use has been found for it as aircraft plywood, for which Black Italian and grey poplar are the best. Matches imported from Sweden are made of aspen.

PRIVET (*Ligustrum vulgare* L.) is scarcely a tree, though in the open and undisturbed it will grow to a height of fifteen feet or more. The greenish twigs are long, slender, and spreading, with very small buds in opposite pairs. As the bush is only half deciduous many of the leaves persist throughout the winter; they are dark green, narrow, pointed, and smooth, and not more than two inches long. Privet grows best on calcareous soils, such as chalk, limestone, and oolite. It puts up with the smoke of towns and stands clipping, though most privet hedges are composed of another species, *Ligustrum ovalifolium* Hasskarl, a native of Japan.

REDWOOD (*Sequoia sempervirens* Endlicher), one of the two Big Trees of California, was introduced in 1846 by Hartweg, a collector for the Horticultural Society of London. Trunk straight and very tall, buttressed at the base in large specimens; bark reddish, spongy, and fibrous. Crown narrow in relation to the height, dark green and pointed. The leaves are small and of two kinds: on the side twigs they are from a quarter to half an inch long and in two ranks; on the terminal shoots they are smaller, not in two ranks, and with hard points curved inward. The tree has the remarkable power for a conifer of sending up stool-shoots and suckers. The timber is red, strong, and durable. According to C. P. Ackers, 'Untreated gateposts of this timber grown in England have been taken up after twenty years' use and have shown no trace of decay.' The wood burns well but very fast and needs constant replenishing.

RHODODENDRON (*Rhododendron ponticum* L.). A native of south-eastern Europe and introduced by Conrad Loddiges in 1763. In 1568 Turner, in his *Herbal*, wrote: 'I have seen this tree in diverse places of Italy; but I care not if it never come into England, seeing it in all points is like a Pharisee: that is, beauteous without, and within a ravenous wolf and murderer.' Most foresters will agree; in heathy soils free from lime it spreads into an impenetrable scrub, and is useless for timber or firewood. The bark is pinkish and the leaves long, thick, and leathery, dark glossy green above, pale green below. It can be distinguished from the cherry laurel, which has similar undesirable habits, by the colour of the bark and the fact that the leaves have no notches.

ROBINIA. *See* ACACIA.

ROWAN. *See* MOUNTAIN ASH.

SILVER FIR (*Abies alba* Miller). A tall fir with a grey smooth bark which becomes scaly in older trees. The branches are whorled in young trees. The needles are arranged in approximately two ranks on either side of the twig and notched at the end, dark green and glossy above and have two white bands running lengthwise underneath. The winter buds are usually in threes, blunt, and free from resin. The cones are upright on the branches and drop their scales, leaving a stiff axis on the tree. The timber is classed with that of spruce and known as White Deal or Whitewood. The fire-wood burns with a strong but pleasant scent, and has heating power equal to that of spruce. The tree was introduced from the continent of Europe in the sixteenth century.

SPANISH, or SWEET, CHESTNUT (*Castanea sativa* Miller) is a large tree with a fissured bark, often twisted and giving a bright brown blaze. It grows to a large size on soils free from lime, and has, when not crowded, a cylindrical head, with horizontal branches drooping at the ends. The buds are distichous on stout angular twigs, each bud having two visible scales, one large and one small. The timber is like that of oak but without the silver grain, and is used as a substitute for it, but is apt to be 'shaky,' i.e. cracked concentrically or radially. Cleft chestnut makes excellent fence posts and palings. Stakes and hop poles last well in the ground. Chestnut underwood fetches high prices in Kent and Sussex. The firewood behaves like larch, crackling and sparking.

SPINDLE (*Euonymus europaeus* L.) is a shrub or small tree having small buds in opposite pairs on greenish four-angled twigs. If the twigs appear cylindrical look for a raised line running down the twig from the leaf-scar directly below the buds; if these are found the twigs almost certainly belong to the spindle tree. As a further aid to identification the bud-scales are green, with red tips or edges. The four-cornered fruits often hang on the tree till Christmas. The wood is white and can be made into knitting needles and piano keys, and has recently been used for manicure

25

outfits. It makes good artist's charcoal; according to J. C. Loudon, a number of shoots of two years' growth are put into an iron tube, and after closing it so as to exclude the air, the tube is put in the fire till it becomes red; it is then taken out, and allowed to cool before the charcoal is removed. The spindle tree, as the name implies, was formerly used for the spindles of hand looms.

SPRUCE (*Picea* A. Dietrich). The best known is the Norway Spruce or Christmas Tree (*Picea Abies* Karsten), a native of northern Europe and introduced in the sixteenth century. Like Silver Fir young trees have whorled branches and erect leading shoot, but the needles when pulled off leave little pegs and not scars. The cones are long, hang down, and drop off as a whole. The cone-scales are thin and without bracts. The bark often has a coppery tinge. The timber is known as Whitewood or White Deal. Most of it comes from Russia and the Baltic. It is white and soft and used for joinery, flooring, matchboardings, packing-cases, food containers, scaffold and ladder poles, pit props, and wood pulp for the manufacture of newsprint. As firewood it is not in the first class, being equal to that of larch and chestnut.

Sitka Spruce (*Picea sitchensis* Carrière), from Alaska and British Columbia, is a fast-growing tree giving an enormous volume of timber per acre in pure plantations. It was introduced by David Douglas in 1831. The prickly needles are longer than those of Norway Spruce and stand out stiffly in all directions, so that the shoots are painful to grasp, and beaters naturally detest it. The under side of the needles is silver-grey. The timber is known to the trade as Silver Spruce and is much used in aircraft construction.

Hemlock Spruce (*Tsuga heterophylla* C. S. Sargent) is a handsome fast-growing tree suitable for underplanting, as it stands a lot of shade. It was brought from the Pacific coast of North America in 1851 by John Jeffrey, collector to the Oregon Association of Edinburgh. Andrew Murray first gave it the name of *Abies Albertiana* in honour of the Prince Consort, patron of the association, and the tree is still called Albertiana by a large number of planters. The branches are not in whorls, while the blunt needles are broader and flatter than those of the true spruces. The leading shoot arches gracefully. The timber, which is better than that of Norway spruce, has been imported in considerable quantities since 1939.

SYCAMORE (*Acer pseudoplatanus* L.), now widely spread over Britain, was not introduced from the Continent until the sixteenth century. The greenish-grey bark is smooth in saplings and poles but scaly and pinkish in older trees, not fissured. The crown passes from a pyramidal or conical shape in young trees to a cylinder with a rounded top in old trees. The main branches spread at a wide angle with the trunk, and droop somewhat at the ends. The twigs are stout, having prominent leaf-scars in opposite pairs, and the smooth buds are yellowish-green, with dark tips and edges. Like ash the tree produces plenty of seedlings, and since rabbits will not eat them if they can get anything else dense thickets of sycamore are frequent near mother trees. They should not be confused with ash, which has stumpy black buds. Squirrels do much damage by gnawing the young branches and twigs. The timber is white, and is useful for furniture, textile rollers, and butchers' blocks; it stands any amount of scrubbing with soap and water and so makes good bread platters, bowls, dairy utensils, and draining-boards for sinks. Poles are turned on the lathe into brush-backs, cotton reels, bobbins, and various small articles. Both the firewood and charcoal are excellent.

TSUGA. *See* SPRUCE.

WALNUT (*Juglans regia* L.), a native of south-east Europe, was introduced probably in Roman times. A middle-sized tree with a short trunk and broad spreading crown. Bark silvery grey, smooth at first, later becoming scaly and furrowed, giving a buff blaze with dark streaks. Twigs stout and fluted, with large heart-shaped leaf-scars. If the twigs are split down the middle with a sharp knife it will be seen that the pith is divided into numerous chambers with thin walls arranged in ladder-like fashion. Fruiting is capricious owing to the danger from late spring frosts. As rooks are fond of the fruit it is better not to plant any trees near a large rookery (A. W. Witt). The timber is greyish brown, with dark smoky streaks, hard, tough, and as strong as oak; it is sought after for high quality furniture and cabinet work, for which the logs should measure at least six feet round. Good seasoned walnut is the best wood there is for gun and rifle stocks. The wood burns well, but does not make good charcoal.

The Black Walnut (*Juglans nigra* L.) is a taller and larger tree with a deeply furrowed brown bark and hairy young twigs.

WAYFARING TREE (*Viburnum Lantana* L.), common on chalk, limestone, and oolite, is a shrub or small tree seldom taller than eighteen feet. It can be recognized in winter by its twigs covered with greenish-white felt and bearing long erect buds in opposite pairs. The buds are really unopened leaves, having no protective scales. The wood is white and hard and may be used for turnery.

WELLINGTONIA (*Sequoia gigantea* Decaisne), one of the two Big Trees of California, was introduced by Messrs. Veitch in 1853 through their collector William Lobb. It is closely related to the redwood and has the same thick spongy bark, tall straight trunk buttressed at the base, and relatively narrow crown with a regular outline. It differs in having none of its leaves in two ranks. Unlike redwood it does not send up fresh shoots from the cut stool. C. P. Ackers says it makes good rough estate timber, but he does not recommend it for wide-scale commercial planting.

WHITE BEAM (*Sorbus Aria* Crantz), practically confined to chalk and limestone though apparently capable of growing on any soil, is a small tree up to thirty feet, with a straight smooth trunk and broad rounded head. The young, much-ringed twigs are brown, stoutish, and tipped with large, green, pointed buds. The wood is hard, close-grained, yellowish-white, and has a strong smell when fresh. It burns well. Like other species of *Sorbus* it is a good ornamental tree for small gardens.

WILD SERVICE (*Sorbus torminalis* Crantz) is now rare. The name Service is derived through various stages from the ancient Latin name *Sorbus*. A middle-sized tree with large trunk spreading at the top into many branches and forming a large crown. Young twigs purplish or glossy brown and dotted with white lenticels. Buds large, green, more or less globular. The wood is like that of White Beam but without the smell.

WILLOW (*Salix* L.). Willow buds have only one scale and are spirally arranged on the twigs. Pollarded willows, so often seen along the banks of streams, usually belong to the Crack Willow (*Salix fragilis* L.) and the White Willow (*Salix alba* L.). Both when not pollarded grow into fair-sized trees. In the former the twigs are hairless and glossy and snap off easily just above their junction with the branch; elsewhere they are, like all willow twigs, very hard to break. In white willow the twigs and buds are covered with silky hairs and the twigs do not snap off in the same way. Osier (*Salix viminalis* L.) has very long velvety twigs. In Sallow or Goat Willow (*Salix caprea* L.) the twigs are hairless or nearly so, often reddish, and with large hairless yellowish buds from which come the yellow erect catkins called 'palm,' because they are used for decorating churches on Palm Sunday. The buds and twigs of Grey Willow (*Salix cinerea* L.) are covered with white cottony hairs.

Other species of willow occur wild, but are less often met with.

28

Purple Willow (*Salix purpurea* L.) has opposite buds. The bark of Almond-leaved Willow (*Salix amygdalina* L.) separates in flakes. The handsome Bay Willow (*Salix pentandra* L.) has glossy brown twigs like those of crack willow, while the buds are egg-shaped and large, more like those of sallow, from which they differ in being polished brown rather than reddish or yellowish. Two varieties of the white willow are worth mentioning: Golden Willow (variety *vitellina* Stokes) whose orange-coloured twigs light up the winter scene, and variety *coerulea* W. D. Koch, the Cricket Bat Willow, of which the branches ascend at an acute angle, giving the tree a remarkably narrow outline (Gilbert-Carter). The Weeping Willow (*Salix babylonica* L.) is said to have been first brought to England about 1730 by Mr. Vernon, a merchant at Aleppo.

Willow wood is white and straight-grained but not durable. It is sometimes used for fencing, as the stakes readily sprout and form a living fence; and for cart bottoms, hurdles, packing-cases, and artificial limbs. The cultivation of the cricket bat willow can be highly profitable if the trees are tended with knowledge and skill. As firewood willow is nearly useless, though it yields medicinal charcoal. The wands of nearly all willows can be grown for basket-making, but the best are obtained from osier, which is widely cultivated for this purpose. Cuttings one or two years old are planted about one foot apart in deep, moist, well-drained soil and carefully hoed, weeded, and thinned. In three years they are fit for cutting into withies for basket-making and wicker-work. The bark of willows contains salicin, from which aspirin is derived. Professor Burnet, in his inaugural address to the Medico-Botanical Society, 1831, reported that three doses of six grains had been known to stop a fever, adding that it was a wise provision of providence in placing the remedy for agues and other low fevers exactly in those moist situations where these diseases are most prevalent (Loudon).

YEW (*Taxus baccata* L.). A dark, gloomy, evergreen conifer with a spreading ragged crown and peeling reddish bark. The leaves are narrow, about an inch long, dark green on the upper side and bright green on the lower, and arranged in two ranks on the twig. The fruit is a small fleshy red cup containing one seed. Though much planted in churchyards and as hedges it is found wild on the Sussex and Hampshire downs and in chalk and limestone tracts elsewhere. The foliage is poisonous, so that areas containing it must be fenced off from horses and cattle. The custom of planting it in churchyards is probably due to its funereal aspect, and as a symbol of immortality on account of its great age; there is evidence that the largest yews are as much as a thousand years old. The wood is reddish brown, and so tough and elastic that it was used for the bows of English archers. For various reasons the wood appears to have been more valued in the Middle Ages that it is now: axle-trees and furniture were made of it, and beds of yew wood were thought to be bug-proof. To-day its principal use is for gate-posts and stakes, though woods such as larch, oak, and chestnut are more popular since they are more readily available and easier to fashion. As fuel it is good.

KEY TO WINTER TWIGS

The first step is to decide whether the twig belongs to a deciduous or an evergreen tree. If deciduous refer to 2 on left-hand side below; if evergreen, to 42 below, and so on.

(Number of illustration given in brackets)

Deciduous	. . . .	2
Evergreen	. . . .	42

2.	Twigs with thorns		3
	Twigs without thorns		6
3.	Buds and leaf-scars in opposite pairs or nearly so, the thorns all terminal . . . . *Buckthorn*		(1)
	Buds and leaf-scars alternate		4
4.	Thorns in pairs, one on either side of an irregular leaf-scar in the centre of which is a practically invisible bud . . . . *Acacia*		(2)
	Thorns solitary, directly above a leaf-scar or terminating the twig and often bearing buds or leaves . .		5
5.	Leaf-scars narrowly crescent-shaped . . *Hawthorn*		(3)
	Leaf-scars broad and rounded . . . *Blackthorn*		(4)
6.	Buds and leaf-scars in opposite pairs or nearly so . .		7
	Buds and leaf-scars alternate		17
7.	Buds and young twigs white- or grey-felted; buds without scales . . . . *Wayfaring Tree*		(5)
	Buds with scales, the twigs not felted . . .		8
8.	Bud enclosed by only one visible scale *Guelder Rose*		(6)
	Bud-scales two or more		9
9.	Lateral buds with two or at the most three scales .		10
	Lateral buds with more than three scales . . .		13

31

10. Terminal bud scarcely larger than lateral . . . 11
    Terminal bud much larger than lateral . . . 12

11. Young twigs usually bright red, sometimes greenish or
    greyish; buds flat, grey . . . *Dogwood* (7)
    Young twigs tawny, older ones corky; buds round,
    brown . . . . . *Field Maple* (8)

12. Buds black or very dark brown, velvety, on greenish-
    grey twigs depressed near the end . . . *Ash* (9)
    Buds bright brown or greenish . . *Norway Maple* (10)

13. Twigs very stout. Terminal bud very large, egg-
    shaped, pointed, sticky or glazed with resin. Leaf-
    scars large, shield-shaped, about as broad as long
    Horse Chestnut (11)
    Terminal bud not sticky, leaf-scars broader across than
    down 14

14. Bud-scales loose, twig rough with large raised lenticels
    Elder (12)
    Bud-scales tight, twig smooth, lenticels small . . 15

15. Twigs stout, leaf-scars large and prominent *Sycamore* (13)
    Twigs slender, leaf-scars small 16

16. Raised lines running down twig from leaf-scars, leaves
    entirely deciduous, twigs often angular *Spindle* (14)
    No raised lines on twig, leaves often persistent, twig
    cylindrical . . . . . . *Privet* (15)

17. Bud without scales, naked, greyish, hairy *Alder Buckthorn* (16)
    Bud enclosed by one or more true scales . . . 18

18. Bud enclosed by only one visible scale . . . 19
    Bud enclosed by two or more visible scales . . 21

19. Buds on distinct stalks, scale violet-coloured *Alder* (17)
    Buds not stalked, scale not violet-coloured . . . 20

20. Buds conical, standing well out from twig and almost
    completely surrounded on all sides by the leaf-scar
    Plane (18)
    Lateral buds more or less erect, not surrounded on all
    sides by the leaf-scar . . . . *Willow* (19)

21. Visible bud-scales two, one large and one small . . 22
    Visible bud-scales three or more 23

22. Twigs angular . . . . *Spanish Chestnut* (20)
    Twigs cylindrical . . . . . *Lime* (21)

23. Twigs scaly, each scale tipped by a small semicircular leaf-scar. Buds globular, set at a wide angle to the twig . . . . . *Larch* (22)

Twigs not scaly, buds erect 24

24. Twigs remarkably thick and fluted, leaf-scars large, heart-shaped, pith chambered . . *Walnut* (23)

Twigs not remarkably thick, leaf-scars small, pith not chambered 25

25. Buds three-quarters to one inch long, narrow and pointed, bright chestnut-brown on zigzag twigs *Beech* (24)

Buds not more than half an inch long . . . 26

26. Buds dark brown, nearly black 27

Buds bright brown, greenish or grey 28

27. Buds large, shining, tipped with long hairs *Mountain Ash* (25)

Buds very small . . . . . . *Elm* (26)

28. Bud-scales fringed with hairs, buds distichous . . 29

Bud-scales hairy all over, or hairless; buds spirally arranged 30

29. Buds long, pointed, angular . . . *Hornbeam* (27)

Buds short and blunt . . . . *Hazel* (28)

30. The terminal buds at the ends of the long shoots in clusters of three or more 31

Terminal buds solitary or in pairs 32

31. Buds hairy, surrounded by thread-like filaments
Turkey Oak (29)

Buds hairless, without thread-like filaments
Common Oak (30)

32. Buds sticky, long-pointed, hairless 33

Buds not sticky; short-pointed or blunt . . . 34

33. Buds narrowly egg-shaped, lateral ones closely pressed to stem, with points turning inward, buds and twigs shining pale brown . . . . *Aspen* (31)

Buds conical, taper-pointed, lateral ones not incurved, twigs angular . . . . *Black Poplar* (32)

34. Buds hairy 35

Buds hairless 37

35. Young twigs mealy . . . . *Grey Poplar* (33)

Young twigs not mealy 36

33

34

AUTHORITIES REFERRED TO IN THE TEXT

ACKERS, C. P. *Practical British Forestry*. Oxford University Press. 1938.

GILBERT-CARTER, H. *Our Catkin-bearing Plants*. Oxford University Press. 1932.

LOUDON, J. C. *Arboretum et Fruticetum Britannicum*. Longmans. 1838.

MELVILLE, R. *Contributions to the Study of British Elms*. *Journal of Botany*, 1938–40.

TANSLEY, A. G. *The British Islands and their Vegetation*. Cambridge University Press. 1939.

VEITCH, JAMES & SONS. *A Manual of the Coniferae*. Royal Exotic Nursery, Chelsea. 1881.

WARD, H. MARSHALL. *Trees*. Cambridge University Press. 1908.

WITT, A. W. *Walnuts*. *Quarterly Journal of Forestry*. 1939.

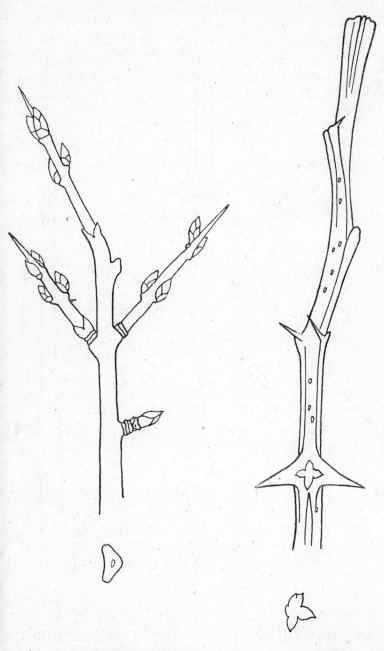

1. BUCKTHORN 2. ACACIA

37

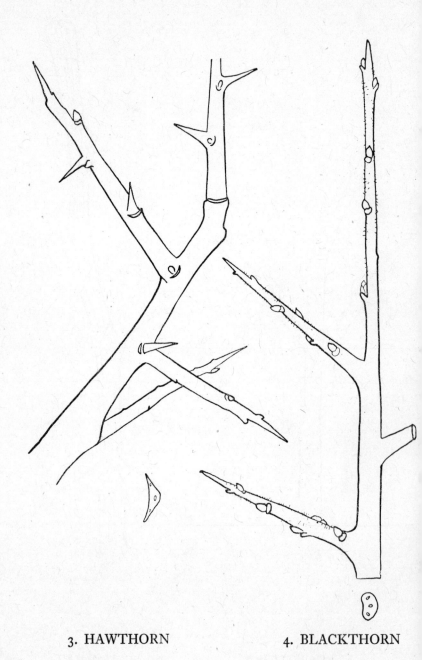

3. HAWTHORN   4. BLACKTHORN

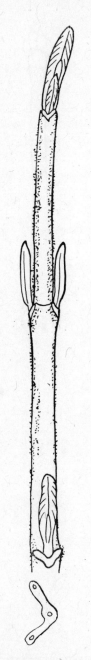

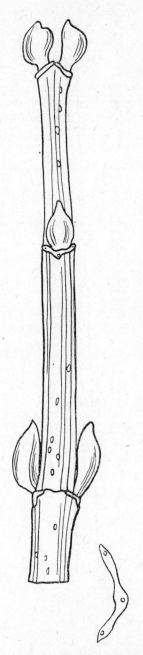

5. WAYFARING TREE   6. GUELDER ROSE

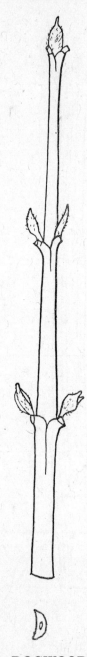

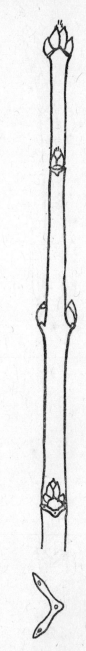

7. DOGWOOD   8. FIELD MAPLE

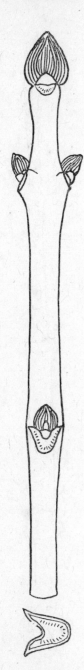

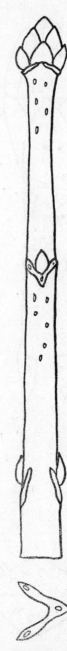

9. ASH   10. NORWAY MAPLE

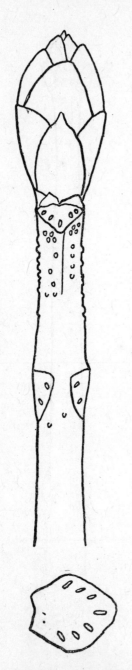

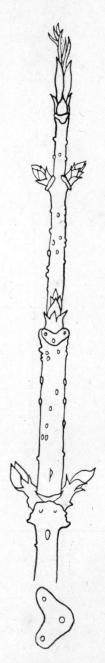

11. HORSE CHESTNUT   12. ELDER

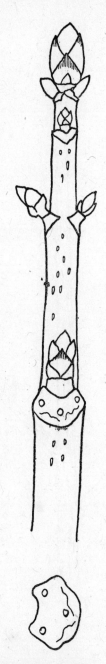

13. SYCAMORE   14. SPINDLE

43

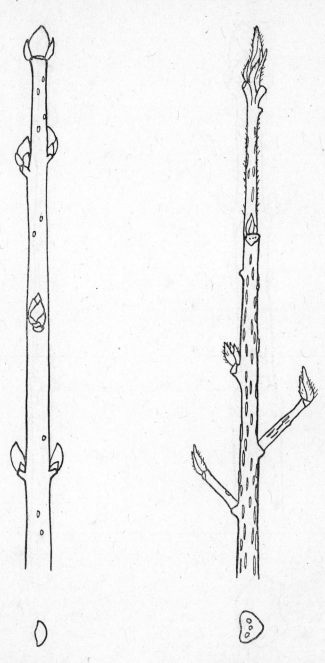

15. PRIVET   16. ALDER BUCKTHORN

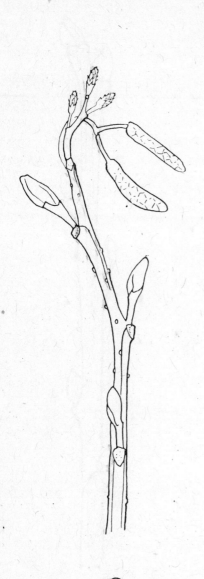

17. ALDER   18. PLANE

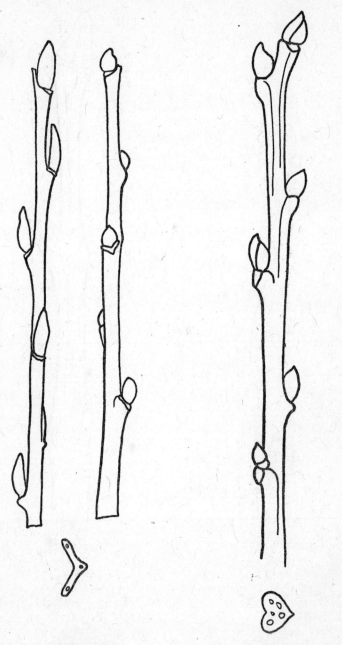

19. WILLOW   20. SPANISH CHESTNUT

46

21. LIME

22. LARCH

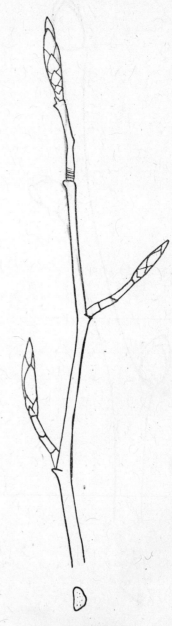

23. WALNUT   24. BEECH

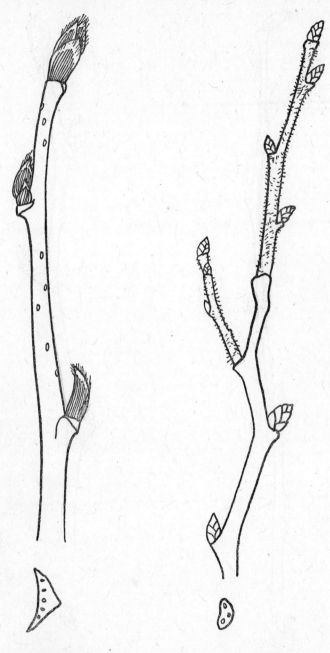

25 MOUNTAIN ASH   26. ELM

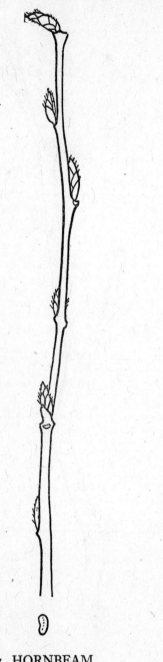

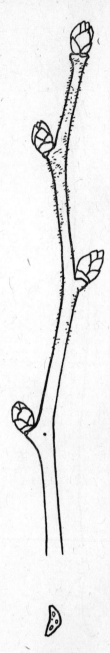

27. HORNBEAM   28. HAZEL

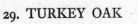

29. TURKEY OAK

30. OAK

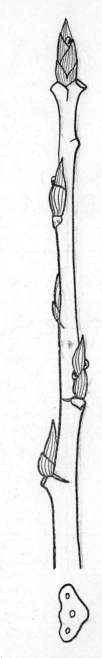

31. ASPEN   32. BLACK POPLAR

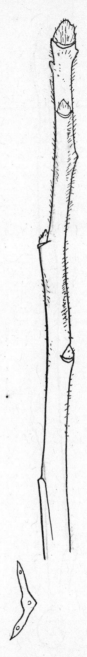

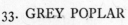

33. GREY POPLAR

34. APPLE

35. PLUM   36. BIRCH

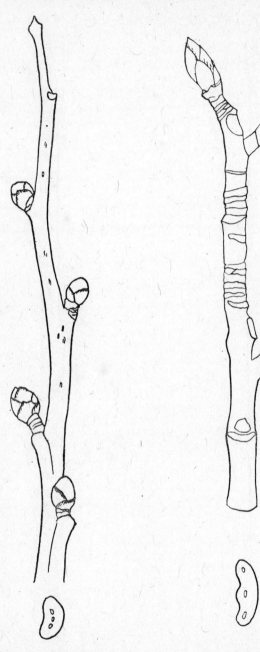

37. WILD SERVICE   38. WHITE BEAM

55

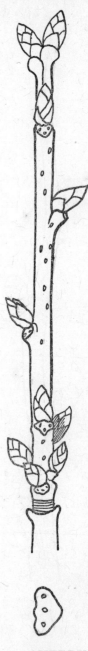

39. PEAR   40. CHERRY